Peter Dixon Books

Creative Expression *(Blackwells)*

Early Years *(Mitchell-Beazley)*

Grow Your Own Poems *(Thomas Nelson)*

Big Billy *(Peche Luna)*

ISBN 1 873195 00 1

I HEARD A SPIDER SOBBING

Peter Dixon

ILLUSTRATED BY DAVID THOMAS

First published 1989
Second Impression 1991
Third Impression 1993
Fourth Impression 1995

Printed by
Sarsen Press,
22 Hyde Street, Winchester.

Further copies are available from
Peche Luna
30 Cheriton Road
Winchester England
SO22 5AX

This book is for 50 year olds who like reading poems for 5 years olds.....

.... and 5 years olds who like reading poems for 15 years olds.

It is for infants, juniors, seniors, mums, dads, grandpops, jolly uncles and aunties who wear funny hats.

It is for lollypop ladies, school-keepers, head-teachers, pie-eaters and people who keep chickens.

It is for people who can't read but like looking at pictures, and for people who don't like looking at pictures but can read.

It is for anyone everywhere. But most of all it is for people who are kind to spiders.

POEMS

Page

I HEARD A SPIDER SOBBING 9

I've always been interested in spiders, and it is important always to write about things that interest you. Mars Bars or Crisps – Horses or Hospitals – Just Anything.

I AM THE LAST 12

The alphabet could start all sorts of poems. Why not try your own.... But call it 'I Am The First', I Am The Biggest....'

PLAYGROUND INCIDENT 14

My cousin and I used to collect little pieces of stone and glass. We thought they were really precious. Well they were to us. What do you collect?

HAPPY DOG DAY 16

Pets are a wonderful starter for poetry, but write about one 'small' incident don't ever try to say too much in a poem. How about a poem about his/her food. Nothing more – just how and what your pet eats.

LITTLE ARNOLD 18

A funny but serious poem. Did you know that they still poison golden eagles in Scotland? There's a start for a poem. 'I'm the man who poisons eagles...' I might start that poem tonight. What makes you really angry?

FLIES 20

What wouldn't you like to be? Perhaps you could write something – but do not use 'flies' or you will find it hard not to copy my words. Poems need to be all your own.

I LOVE 21

Well your poem could be 'I HATE'. Make sure it is what you really 'feel'. Not what sounds right. Go for the truth.

CHILDBURST 23

I often watch children at playtime. That's why the poem was fairly easy to write. Who or what do you watch?

TOOTHPASTE 26

Often people think poems have to be written about 'proper' things such as 'The Wind' or 'Flowers'. Anything you feel interested or happy or even annoyed about will make an excellent poem.

SANDWITCHES 27

This poem came from a spelling mistake. Often things that 'go wrong' give a start for a new idea. Look very carefully before you throw any words or ideas away.

I HEARD A SPIDER SOBBING

I heard a spider sobbing
Deep in an autumn day.
She was sobbing in the bushes
Where spiders spin away.

Her legs were wet with spider tears,
Her eyes as full as seas.
There were blisters on her fingers
And blisters on her knees.

I held her in my warmcup hands.
I watched her wipe her tears
And whisper things and tell me things
Of spiders and their fears.

"I cannot weave a web" she said
"I don't know how it goes.
It gets in such a muddle,
It tangles in my toes.

The silk – it all gets muddled
It hooks up on my knees,
Then catches in the bushes
And blows in all the breeze.

I cannot get it right" she cried.
"It's such an awful mess.
A great big spider tangle,
A massive blackbird nest.

The other spiders giggle
They crawl across to laugh
And call me clumsy fingers
And say that I am daft.

They always call me stupid,
They always make me cry
And I've never caught an insect,
or moth
or bug
or fly.

I've never caught a single thing,
My web's no good at all.
It's just a tatty tangle
A sort of cobweb ball.

It's a great big mass of muddle
It's a matted messy mat.
It fell off all the bushes
And it landed on the cat"

I gazed upon the sleeping Tom
The tortured web hung dead.
A weave of tangled tangles....
.... the spider shook her head.

Her eyes again were flooded.
A sobbing shook my hand
So –
I took her very gently
To a special kind of land ....

A land I know for spiders
Who cannot weave a trap
Where everyone is happy
With spiders big and fat.
A land of flies and honey
A land where all is lace,
And no-one needs to worry
or spin
or weave
or race.

My land is very secret.
I cannot tell you where.
But if you ask a spider

then

she

might

take you there.

I AM THE LAST:

Ant in the Hill
Bird in the Bush
Cat of the Nap
Daisy in the Chain
Egg of a Dodo
Feather in the Cap
Gnome in the Garden
Hole in a Polo
Eye of a Needle
Jack in the Box
King of the Castle
Light of the Day
Mile of the Way
Nail in the Coffin
Orange in the Squash
Pat on the Back
Question in the Quiz
Rap on the Door
Sting in the Tail
Toad in the Hole
U in the Bend
Viper in the Nest
Wish in the Well
X of a Lover
Ya of the Hoo
Zebra on the Crossing

WHO SAID WHERE?
WHEN

PLAYGROUND INCIDENT

Please Miss –
At play I had a precious stone worth
a thousand pounds
I showed it first to Betsy Smith
And then to Lizzie Jones.
Josey Watkins had a look
And Liza Robson too –
Then Michael West
He slapped my hand
And kicked it with his shoe.

Well Tony Murray only laughed
And so did Elkie Gray,
Then all the other Class 2 girls
Just laughed – and ran away.
They pulled my hair
They pushed me too
They said my stone was glass
And my white skirt got all stained up
With green stuff – off the grass...

They said that I was stupid, Miss
They went and made my cry
And Lizzie Jones she got a stick
And threw it near my eye.
They splashed a great big puddle, Miss
They threw some muddy mess
It got all on me cardigan
It's got all on me dress.

.... My Mum won't half be angry, Miss
My Mum won't half be mad.
She'll come up school and see you... Miss
She'll Come up with me Dad.

She'll come up with me Auntie too.
She'll bring my Nan as well.
So –
Shall I go and fetch her now –

Or wait until the bell?

HAPPY DOGDAY

Today –
Is our dog's birthday.

It's Happydogdayday.
Sixteen years of panting
And sixteen years of play.

Sixteen years of dogtime.
Sixteen years of barks
– eating smelly dog food
And making muddy marks.

It's a hundred years of our time.
It's a hundred human years
– of digging in the garden
and scratching itchy ears.
It's a hundred years of living rooms
(he never goes upstairs)
and dropping hairy whiskers
and being pushed off chairs...

It's a hundred years of being with us
A hundred years of Dad,
and a hundred of my sister
(that must be really bad!)

So:
No wonder he looks really old
No wonder he is grey
And cannot hear
Or jump
Or catch
Or even run away.....
No wonder that he sleeps all day,
No wonder that he's fat
And only dreams of catching things
and chasing neighbours cats....

So fight your fights
In dogdream nights
Deep within your bed...

today's your day
and we all say ....

LITTLE ARNOLD AND THE DODO

One day
Little Arnold found a Dodo.
He found it in the park,
Right behind some bushes
Where it was very dark.

Little Arnold took the Dodo
And put it in a box,
And kept it in the cellar
In a nest he made of socks.

Little Arnold loved the Dodo
He fed it every day,
And told it Dodo stories
So it wouldn't go away.

He told it tales of wonder
He told it tales of life
Then he went and searched for others –
All Dodos need a wife.

He searched for many hours,
He sought both high and low.
Then saw one in the bushes
Where Dodos like to go.

"Oh come here, Mrs Dodo"
Good Little Arnold cried,
"I have a Dodo man for you,"
And Mrs Dodo sighed.

So now they have a Dodo nest,
Mr Dodo has a bride.
They lay a Dodo egg a day,
and Arnold has it –
fried.

FLIES

I would not like to be a fly
they don't last long before they die.
Their deaths you see –
are always nasty,
like –
being baked inside a pasty.
Others die in smelly places,
or slapped to death on people's faces.
Small ones die on spray for roses
or stuck in stuff up people's noses.
Fat ones die in deaths as quick
– stick in jam
– or pools of sick....
Other die on window panes
rubbish tips
and stopped up drains.
Blow flies – die in boiling haddock
or chewed to death in people's faggots...

So – I'd hate to be a fly.

There must be better ways to die.

I LOVE :

Lumpy gravy
Black sauce on tomato ketchup tops
Greasy plates
Split teabags
Losing keys
And split nails

I love:
Getting up on Mondays
Cold flannels
Broken laces
Spilt sugar
Chaps
Raps
Silver paper on fillings
and watery cabbage.

I love:
Tangles
Grazes
Grumpy Teachers
And assemblies that go on and on
and on
and on

for hours and hours
and hour
and hours
but most of all –

I love
Telling
Great
Big
Bulgy
Fat

..... fibs

CHILDBURST

It's playtime... it's childburst
and out they all run
Daniel slips over
and falls on his thumb.
Allison's fizzing
her ribbons aflame
Donna's a donkey
and Roger's a crane.
Cindy is squealing
and Cynthia skips
Marcus is laughing
and spitting out crisps.
Daren is fighting
and Emma's in tears
she's stuck in the railing
– right up to her ears.
Jacko is jumping
he's on Simon's back
his nose needs a wiping
his fingers are black,
he's bellowing,
        yelling,
        pulling at hair
he knows how to fight
and he knows how to swear!
The puddle's in motion
it's splashing around
it's on Jacko's jacket
and Janice is drowned.

It's splashing and leaping
right up to the sky
it's on every nose
and it's in every eye.
The dustbins are shaking
they want to join in
they throw off their hats
and they dance to the din.
There's hidings
and seeking
        pushings
and squeals,
chasing of skirts
and dizzy cartwheels.
There's comics to flutter
to chase in the breeze
plasters in cloakrooms
and scabs on the knees.
The gate is a palace,
this pebble a gem,
the step is a mountain,
the wall is a den....
Quick!
hide in the corner
but keep off the ground,
if your foot touches tarmac
you're bound to be found.

We'll scream and we'll bellow
we'll spit and we'll roar
hide in the toilets
and hold back the door.

Look!

Teachers are coming!
their thunderer blows
'stand with a partner
        walk in on your toes...'
Playtime is over
so walk back in twos
it's time for the telly
        and writing your news.

WHO STRANGLED THE TOOTHPASTE?

This morning ...
After Weetabix,
I discovered
Toothpaste...
Capless,
Dented,
torn and twisted,
Oozing lifepaste
On white porcelain.

'Not I...' hissed cold tap.
'Nor I ....' dripped her brother.
Not 'ussssssss'
And there he lies
bloated,
Battered,
Twisted as a pompidom
By his vase of bright stemmed flowers.

And it wasn't me.
and it wasn't my brother.
and it wasn't my mother
......
I think it was Dad.

He's downstairs drowning teabags
and beating up the eggs.

SANDWITCHES

Witches live on beaches,
They come out in the night.
They live in caves of seaweed
And blowout lighthouse lights.

They laugh at shipwrecked sailors,
They shriek like herring gulls
And, when they want to giggle,
They go on seal-pup culls.

They ride on dead sea horses.
They gallop through the rocks
And look for people swimming
And steal their pants and socks.

They bury them in witch holes
Burrowed in the sand
And no-one ever finds them
In deepest Sandwitch Land.

They squint about for children
And find them as they play
And knock down all their castles
And wreck their holiday.

They kick sand in their faces,
Knock ice-cream out of cones,
Make children fall in rock-pools
And cut themselves on stones.

They spoil all beach parties,
They ruin all beach games,
And puncture all the beachballs
And call the children names.

They sprinkle sand on picnics,
Drop shingle in the cakes,
And stir up all the sandflies
And melt the chocolate flakes.

They rain on Punch and Judy,
Make your parking place a lake.
Make your candyfloss all soggy
And make the deck-chairs break.

So if you're playing at the seaside
When the surf is rolling high
And you hear the seagulls shrieking,
But see none in the sky,

Then run and find your mother,
Then run and hide away....
For the Sandwitches are coming
And it's you they want today!

YORKY (A Yorkshire Spaceman)

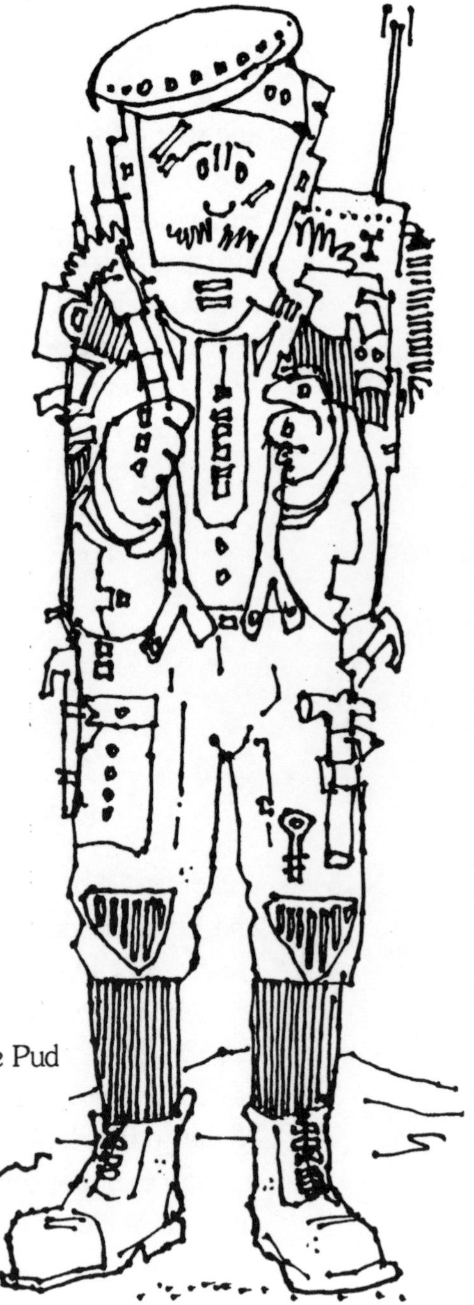

Yorky – was a Yorkshireman
he lived in Yorkshireland.
He built himself a spaceship
(but it wasn't very grand).

He couldn't get the proper wire
and he couldn't get the wood,
so he built it out of rubbish stuff
(and lumps of Yorkshire pud).

The nose cone was a crusty bit
the fins were made of dough –
but when poor Yorky started it
his spaceship wouldn't go.
... the jet bit hissed,
it spat,
it roared .....
great clouds of smoke arose –
and shot inside his helmet
and it shot right up his nose!
He couldn't see,
He hicked,
He coughed,
He wriggled in his seat,
and saw fat chunks of Yorkshire Pud
sizzle round his feet.

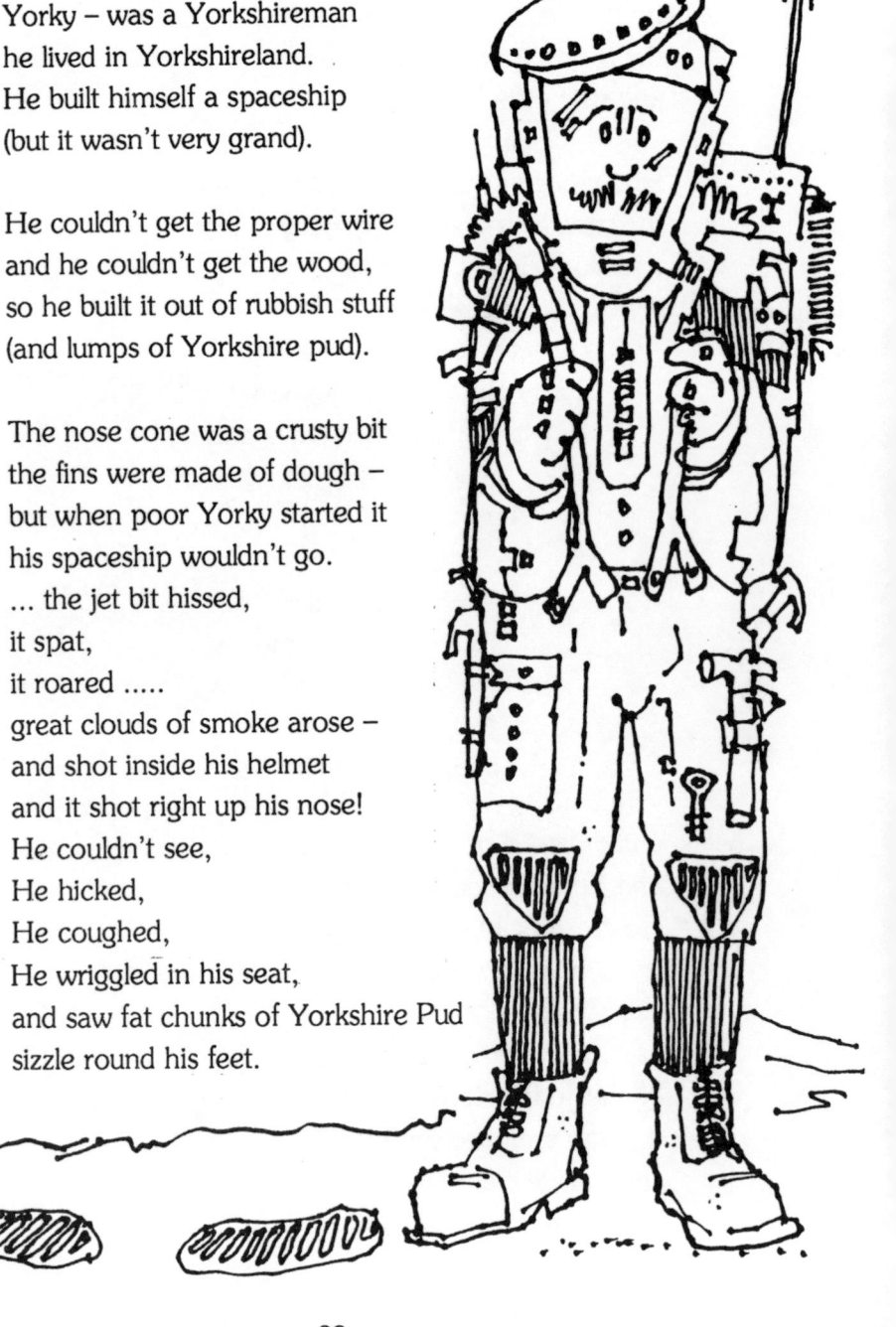

Well –
Yorky gave an awful YELL
his heartbeat gave a race –
the rocket gave a mighty heave
and shot off –
into space!
Hot lumps of Pud came raining down
the crowds waved their goodbyes –
and Yorky in his batter seat
wiped his battered eyes.
He set a course for Milky Way
(turn right at just gone Mars)
and sat and watched strange thing
go
by
like...
comets,
moons
and stars.

Brave Yorky travelled ten light years but then got very bored
and dreamed of sunny Yorkshire Land
and Yorkshire cricket scores.
He dreamed of steaming Yorkshire Pud
gravy round it's crust
crispy juicy edges
as dark and brown as rust.
He heard the clank of batter tins
the pop of puffed up Puds
chewy little pieces
and pretty Yorkshire woods.

I must get down
he sighed,
he cried,
I must return to York....
So Yorky in his Yorkshire way
began a spaceman walk.
He's walking now – at midnight hour
He walks from star to star
and smells the smell of pudding
afar
afar
afar.....
He's walking when you're warm in bed.
he walks through every night,
so think of him
and dream of him
when you turn out
the light.

VISITING WINCHESTER COLLEGE

Cloisters War Memorial – Autumn —81

Who are you, Aubrey Sawyerr
With two R's instead of one.
Who were you, Aubrey Sawyerr
Did you stab, and kill, and run?
Did you spring from muddied trenches?
Did you lead your men to fight?
Did you drown in shell shocked terror
In holes of mud at night?
Who were you, Aubrey Sawyer??
Did you whistle city girls?
Where your eyes as bright as marbles?
Was your hair a sea of curls?
Did you chase around these cloisters
Can we hear your schoolboy laugh,
Can we watch your boater spinning
And see your football scarf?
Can we read your cricket score card,
Can we hear you in the choir?
And see you toasting muffins
Around the prefect's fire?
Can we see you win the silver sword,
Can we see you passing out –
And see you score the winning goal
And hear the first form shout?
'Hurrah, for good old Sawyerr'
(with two RR's instead of one)
He led the school to victory
And now he's got a gun.

Oh, where are you, Aubrey Sawyerr,
The farmer's soil's your home.
Eyes as black as carbon
Boots on rods of bone.
Did they kill you very quickly?
Or did you slowly die –
In fields of blood and poppies.
In fields of gas and flies?
Don't tell us, Aubrey Sawyerr,
Our day is soft and blue.
But when we walk together
Then we will talk of you.

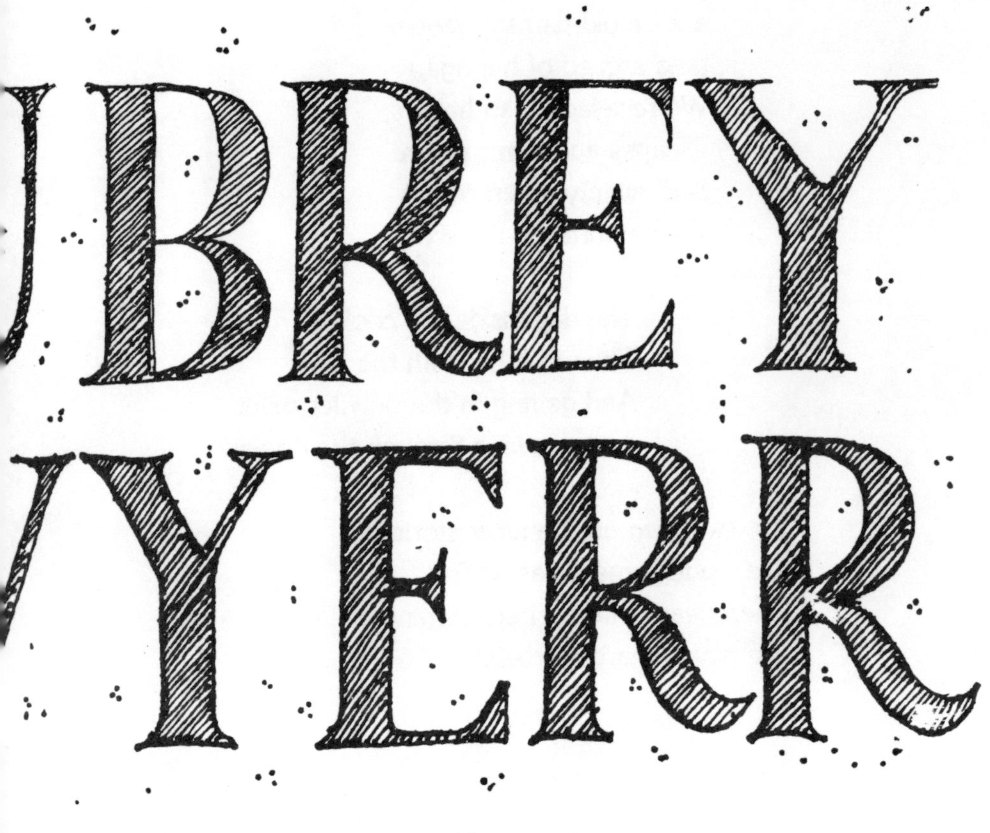

QUEENIE

Our hamster died at playtime
Beside her silver wheel,
Closed her eyes for ever
(she ate some orange peel.)
She closed her eyes for ever
She twitched her nose no more,
A sleeping looking hamster
(except she couldn't snore)....

Yes,
Queenie died at playtime
We gathered round her cage
and retold hamster stories
(and argued of her age.)
We recalled bitten fingers,
Escapes and hunts galore
And twenty seven babies
– adventures by the score.

The day inside the cooker
The week beneath the floor
And getting in the powder paint
And gnawing through the door.

We swapped our hamster stories
(we made some up as well)
Then heard the teachers coming
(we never heard the bell.)

"The hamster's dead, Miss Simmonds,
The hamster's just gone dead –
And have a look, Miss Simmonds –
a fly's got on its head."

Miss Simmonds ordered silence
Demanded – "Look this way.....
It's half past ten, and Thursday,
And time for work not play."

AN AWFUL TALE
Uncle Sid (a gardening man)

Uncle Sid grew turnips
as big as north sea mines,
Taties fat as pillows,
beans like railway lines.
Radishes like beach balls,
cauliflowers like clouds,
Sprouts as tight as walnuts

..... AND SLUGS LIKE FOOTBALL CROWDS.
They crept our late one evening
as uncle cleaned his spade,
A silent sliding army
a silver slug parade.
My uncle saw them coming
He hid behind his shed
waiting for the onslaught
– beside his beetroot bed.
We heard his cry of battle
we saw him in the sprouts
dubbined boots a-kicking
bellows,
yells
and shouts.
We saw him turn the first attack,
we watched them form their square,
We saw him hurl his pellets
and spit and stamp and swear.

The enemy retreated
then wheeled across his rear
– he hurled a thousand plant pots
and gave his battle cheer.
Yet –
their army never faltered their ranks stayed firm and wet,
orange speckles glinting,
flanks as black as jet.

...

He fled towards his garden shed
the door – he jammed with sticks
he filled the holes with sacking
and glass
        and stones
                and bricks.

They found him
dawn
next morning,
the garden rich and green,
not a cabbage leaf was nibbled
nor a bite from any bean.
The pumpkins smiled with fatness
the lettuces were sound
a thousand slugs lay smitten...
                bodies all around.
Five hundred in the trenches
– others on the stones

and Uncle Sid
a hero

but Uncle Sid
was bones.

BOMBLAST!

Bomblast! Bomblast! Come on out!
That's what all the children shout.
Bomblast! Bomblast! One, two, three
Bomblast! Bomblast! Can't catch me!

Bomblast! Bomblast! Kick his door!
Said he was a soldier in 1944...
Said he was a gunner in a place called France...
Rattle on his door-knob and watch him
dance!

Said he was a soldier in the King's Grenadiers,
Said he'd been a prisoner and fought for years,
Said he's been a sergeant, said he'd fought the hun,
Said he'd fought with hand-grenade,
with bayonet, blade and gun.

Said he'd been a hero,
Said he's saved men's lives,
And now he lives in Stanley Street
At number fifty five.

He's old and worn and grumpy,
His eyes are black and sad,
He never cleans his windows
And the big boys say he's mad.

So it's **Up and In and at him!**
And it's **Kick and knock and run!**
And it's **Catch us Mr Bomblast!**
Catch us if you can!

So it's **Bomblast! Bomblast! One, two, three**
Bomblast! Bomblast!

what's a V.C.?

PILLAR BOXES

Are pillar boxes happy?
They don't seem to have much fun
they never go to discos
or dance
or skip
or run....
They only seem to stand around
in wind... and rain – and snow
cold as iron all over
with nowhere much to go.

They always seem to stand alone
lonely as can be
..
all alone at Midnight
                six and ten
                and three
They have no friends
or jokes
or games
No telly, books or laughs
giggles in the corner
... or postbox motor cars.
You never see them singing
or at a swimming pool
or playing silly whatsits
or playing silly fools.

They never nibble chocolate
– lick a strawberry ice
eat a plate of curry
or Chinese things with rice.

They miss on all the best things
They miss out more than most....
But unlike clever humans....

they

never

miss

The Post

RUNNER BEANS

There they stand
Red eyed,
And tall
Proudly clothing yesterday's
Gaspipe
Watermain
and gutted remainder of Uncle Ron's sprung
mattress
Rustling,
Waving,
And winding
A sinewed world on rusted wire
tangled twine
And orange spotted deadwood.

The bean is not a proud legume.

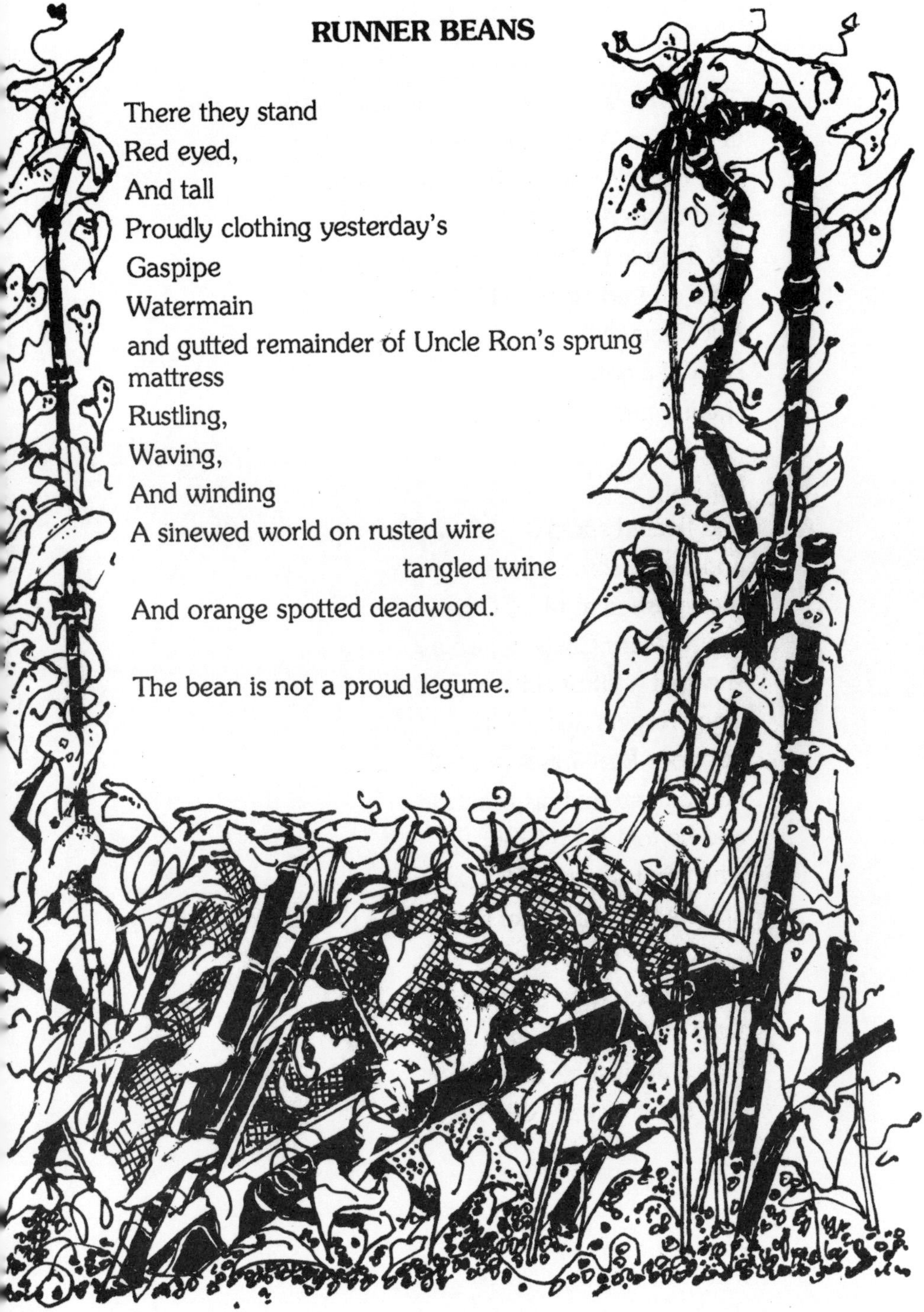

BLOCKED DRAIN

The drain is blocked with a football sock
(and Keep Away said Sir).
The water's murky, the water's dirty
(and Keep Away said Sir).
It's deep and slimey, brown and grimey,
(so Don't go Near, said Sir).
But Lizzie did,
she did a dare,
she jumped it right across

(almost),
and floated sticks
and threw some bricks
then pushed at Mary Cross.
Well – Mary Cross got angry,
she spat a bit of spit,
Tony Rogers dodged it –
but poor Ben Jones got hit!
He ran and told his brother
and he told Rory Cray
who went and told Big Dawkins
and he fetched Porky Day.
. . .
Porky Day came runnin'
then tripped on Tigger's boot,
he fell against his sister
and she knocked Sally Root.
. . .

Sally Root went flying.
A S-P-L-A-S-H
as black as jet...
Her dress awash with water
Her knickers soaking wet.
The juniors all went silent,
the infants ran away,
tears plopped into the puddle
then up came Porky Day...
He laughed and splashed her even more.
He poked her with a stick
and flipped a lot of muddy stuff
that smelt like puddle sick.
He laughed and kicked a great big splash
He went to do some more
        then –
came a mighty thunder
a sort of puddle roar.

The puddle rose
a mushroom form
of stinking sock and slime
ripples brown as cocoa
a smell like farmyard swine.
It hovered over Porky Day
his eyes were filled with dread
the puddle gave a tremble
then jumped right on his head!

Poor Porky lay awash with slosh
an infant called 'Hooray'..

the puddle grinned
and gurgled
then quietly
ran away

CHICKEN-SPOTS

I've got these really itchy spots,
they're climbing on my tummy.
They're on my head,
they're on my tail
and it isn't very funny.
They came to see me yesterday
– a few the day before
Fifty on my bottom
and twenty on my jaw.

I've got a prize one on my toe,
a dozen on my knee
and now they're on my thingy
– I think there's thirty three!

I count them every evening,
I give them names like Fred –
Charlie, Di and Daisy....
Chunky, Tom and Ted.

They're really awful spotties
they drive me itchy mad
the sort of itchy itches
I wish I never had.
Nobby's worst at itching
Lizzie's awful too
and – if you come to see me
I'll give a few to you....
I'll give you Di and Daisy

I'll give you Jane and Ted,
a bucket full of itchers
to take home to your bed...

You can give them to your sister
I don't care what you do.
Give them to a teacher
or send them to the zoo.
I don't mind where you take 'em
I don't care where they go.....

stick them up the chimney
or in the baby's po.
Take them to a farmyard.
Find a chicken pen
and say that they're a present

with love

from me

... to them.

BREAKING FRIENDS WITH SHARON

I've broken friends with Sharon
she's broken friends with me.
I told her I don't like her,
she said she don't like me.
Sharon's really silly
Sharon never shares,
snatches pens and peanuts
Sharon even swears.

Sharon – we don't play now
Sharon plays with Jo
and I don't go to brownies –
– not if Sharon goes.

She told Miss Andrews of me,
she told my sister lies.
I think her new coat's awful
her face,
her smile
and eyes.
I think she's really nasty,
I'd love to see her go,
but one thing's really awkward....
what if she says –

'Hello'

CHARLES

Charles was super,
Brave and sleek.
Head of School
And strong as teak.

Charles was leader,
Charles was best.
Led the School
With style and zest.

Charles was kingly,
Charles was smart.
Kindly eye
And golden heart.

He led through storms
And placid days
With towering strength
And peaceful ways.

............................He was.....................................

The Prince of Whales.